Phonic Book 2a by H

G000298670

Introduction

Phonic Book 2a is one of a series of five books designed to help teach the Phonic Programme outlined in The National Literacy Strategy.

Phonic Book R is aimed at the Reception class. Phonic Books 1a & 1b cover the work for Year 1. Phonic Books 2a & 2b cover the work for Year 2.

Each book is designed to facilitate word building skills. The photocopiable worksheets are aimed to be an aid for the busy primary classroom teacher, preparing word level work for the Literacy Hour. The photocopiable sheets contain a variety of activities - cloze procedure, muddled sentences, tracking activities, word crosses, proof reading and word searches. Much use is made of "Word Building Trains" to encourage children to build their own words. All of these activities aim to reinforce phonic blends until they become automatic to the child.

These books can be used in conjunction with the Read, Write and Spell series of six books which cover the High and Medium Frequency Words outlined in the National Literacy Strategy available directly from Topical Resources.

Topical Resources publishes a range of Educational Materials for use in Primary Schools and Pre-School Nurseries and Playgroups.

For latest catalogue:
Tel: 01772 863158
Fax: 01772 866153

E.Mail:sales@topical-resources.co.uk
Visit our Website on:
www.topical-resources.co.uk

Copyright © 2000 Heather Bell
Illustrated by Pat Lamb

Printed in Great Britain for "Topical Resources", Publishers of Educational Materials, P.O. Box 329, Broughton, Preston, PR3 5LT by T.Snape & Company Ltd, Boltons Court, Preston.
Cover design and layout by
Paul Sealey Illustration & Design, 3 Wentworth Drive, Thornton

First Published January 2000
ISBN 1 872977 51 0

Contents

Teacher's Notes

This book is designed to facilitate phonic word building skills. The photocopiable worksheets are aimed to be an aid for the busy primary classroom teacher, preparing word level work for the literacy hour. The photocopiable sheets contain a variety of activities - cloze procedure, muddled sentences, tracking activities, word crosses, proof reading and word searches. These aim to reinforce phonic blends until they become automatic to the child.

Phonic Word Lists

At the front of books 1a, 1b, 2a and 2b you will find phonic lists of words which can be used as weekly spelling lists. The children should learn no more than fifteen in a week which should be copied into a spelling book, to go home with them. Parents can be encouraged to get the children to practise their spellings by writing them down. Evidence shows that they will be more likely to be retained in the child's visual memory by practising this way rather than orally. Children should be encouraged to write their list down in cursive handwriting. Again, evidence shows this aids memory. Children might also be encouraged to practise spelling lists on the computer. A type size of between 12 and 18 point text should be used.

Children should be encouraged to segment words they are learning to spell ie; break a word or part of a word down into its component phonemes (eg; c-a-t; ch-ar-t; g-r-ou-n-d).
They should also be encouraged to use the "look, say, cover, write, check" strategy to help commit new words to memory.

Phonic Record

This is an individual record of the phonic blends covered in books R, 1a, 1b, 2a and 2b. Copies of the Phonic Record Sheet can be found near the beginning of Books 1a, 1b, 2a and 2b only.(Book R contains a Letter Recognition Record Sheet.) These can be particularly useful when setting Individual Education Plans for Special Needs children with spelling problems. They can also be used as a spelling/phonic record to follow the child through the school.

Word Building Trains

The word building trains often found at the beginning of the phonic activity sheets are a vital part of developing word building skills. They can be copied onto the board and be the starting point of the phonic lesson. Children can be encouraged to find words and then act them out for others to guess what they are. They could also give the other children in the group verbal clues for them to guess the word.It can also be useful for the children to help decide on the most useful words from those built, to put in their weekly spelling list. They thus feel more involved and are more likely to learn words they have chosen.

It is important to remember that much discussion and word building practice should take place either individually, in a small group or in a whole class situation before a child attempts any of the written exercises.

Homework

Books 1a, 1b, 2a and 2b all contain revision exercises to remind children of how to build words they have encountered in previous lessons. These activities would be suitable for written homework tasks provided an adult reminds the children of the sounds being used.

Alf and Bet

The cartoon characters Alf and Bet are used to introduce the activities on each page. The same characters are used in the parallel series of books Read, Write and Spell High Frequency Words. Over a period of time the children will become familiar with these two characters and the activities they are asked to do gradually becoming more independent in their work.

Certificates

Alf and Bet Word Sound Reward Certificates can be found on page 6 of Phonic Book 2a. These can be used to encourage children in their progress through their phonic work. A simpler version dealing with individual letters can be found on page 64 of Book R.

High Frequency Words

Topical Resources publishes a parallel series of books to help pupils Read, Write and Spell High Frequency Words. (For more details, ring 01772 863158 and ask for a catalogue.)

Phonic Blend Record Sheet   Name: _____

Phonic Book R		fr- (frog)		sk (flask)		ew (flew)	
Reception		gl- (glad)		-lp (help)		ue (blue)	
ch- (chin)		gr- (grin)		-mp (jump)		**Phonic Book 2A**	
sh- (shop)		pl- (plum)		-sp (crisp)		**Year 2 Term 1**	
th- (thin)		pr- (pram		-ct (fact)		**Vowel phonemes**	
th- (this)		sc- (scab)		-ft (lift)			
Phonic Book 1A		sk- (skip)		-lt (belt)		u (full)	
Year 1 Term 1		sl- (slip)		-nt (bent)		oo (book)	
Short vowel		sm- (smack)		-pt (slept)		ar (car)	
sounds (cvc)		sn- (snip)		-st (lost)		oy (toy)	
		sp- (spot)		-xt (next)		oi (boil)	
-a- (cat)		st- (stop)		-lf (self)		ow (cow)	
-e- (hen)		sw- (swim)		-nch (bunch)		ou (shout)	
-i- (bin)		tr- (trip)		-lth (health)		**Year 2 Term 2**	
-o- (pot)		tw- (twin)				air (chair)	
-u- (cut)		**Initial consonant**		**Year 1 Term 3**		are (care)	
Year 1 Term 2		**cluster (3 letters)**		**Long vowel**		ere (there)	
word endings				**phonemes**		ear (bear)	
		scr- (scrap)				or (horn)	
-ck (duck)		shr- (shred)		ee (feet)		oor (door)	
-ff (off)		spl- (splash)		ea (sea)		aw (draw)	
-ll (doll)		spr- (spring)		ai (train)		au (caught)	
-ss (miss)		squ- (squash)		a-e (hate)		ore (store)	
-ng (sing)		str- (string)		ay (play)		er (herb)	
Initial consonant		thr- (thrush)		ie (lie)		ir (bird)	
clusters (2 letters)		**Phonic Book 1B**		i-e (bite)		ur (burn)	
bl- (black)		**Common end**		igh (night)		**Year 2 Term 3**	
br- (bring)		**clusters**		y (fly)		ear (hear)	
cl- (clap)				oa (boat)		ea (head)	
cr- (crab)		-ld (old)		o-e (hole)		**Phonic Book 2B**	
dr- (drop)		-nd (land)		ow (show)		**Revision Year 2**	
dw- (dwell)		-lk (milk)		oo (moon)			
fl- (flag)		-nk (think)		u-e (tune)			

Phonic Word Lists

Year2 Term1 - Revision lists of long vowel work from Year 1 Term 3

ee

ee	ea
feet	sea
meet	tea
keep	seat
see	year
seed	fear
seen	jeans
been	clean
heel	teach
feel	beach
week	leaf

ai

ai	a-e	ay
rain	name	play
train	same	day
stain	came	say
brain	game	way
pain	take	away
wait	cake	pray
nail	bake	tray
sail	make	stay
tail	rake	clay
paid	gate	today

ie

ie	i-e	igh	y
lie	bite	high	fly
pie	white	sigh	sly
tie	nine	night	try
die	line	right	dry
tied	shine	light	cry
died	time	fight	fry
lied	like	sight	spy
	bike	tight	by
	side	flight	my
	wide	fright	shy

oa

oa	o-e	ow
boat	bone	show
coat	cone	know
goat	hope	row
float	rope	sow
road	mole	grow
load	hole	throw
toad	pole	snow
toast	stole	blow
roast	home	bowl
soap	store	mower

oo

oo	u-e	ew	ue
moon	tune	flew	blue
soon	June	blew	clue
room	tube	chew	true
boot	cube	drew	due
roof	rude	threw	glue
pool	use	grew	gluing
cool	used	stew	glued
school	cute	brew	
zoo	flute	new	
hoop	rule	few	

Phonic Word Lists Year2 Term1 - Vowel Phoneme word lists

oo short

oo	u
book ✓	pull
look	full
took	bull
cook	pulled
hook	pulling
good	
hood	
wood	
wool	
shook	

ar

ar
car
star
arm
harm
farm
bark
dark
park
sharp
card

oy

oy	oi ✓
toy	oil
boy	soil
joy	boil
enjoy	foil
enjoying	spoil
annoy	coin
annoyed	join
royal	joint
loyal	point
cowboy	noise

ou

ow	ou
cow	out
now	shout
how	our
down	hour
town	flour
brown	mouth
flower	round
shower	pound
owl	sound
crowd	ground

air

air	are	ere	ear
air	care	there	bear
hair	bare	where	wear
fair	rare		tear
pair	dare		swear
lair	fare		wearing
repair	share		tearing
stairs	stare		swearing
chair	Clare		
hairy	glare		
fairy	square		

or

or	oor	aw	au ✓	ore
or	door	claw	caught	more
for	floor	saw	taught	store
sort	poor	raw	naughty	core
short	moor	draw	daughter	snore
sport		jaw	sauce	score
fork		paw	saucer	shore
north		drawer	August	sore
horn		prawn	pause	before
storm		lawn	cause	bore
morning		crawl	because	bored

er

er	ir	ur
her	bird	fur
herb	third	church
kerb	girl	curl
verb	first	burst
perm	shirt	burn
germ	skirt	burnt
term	dirty	turn
verse	birth	hurt
perch	birthday	nurse
herd	sir	purse

Year 2 Term 3

ear	ea
hear	bread
rear	head
fear	dead
tear	read
dear	lead
year	dread
gear	spread
clear	weather
spear	leather
shear	feather

5

Well done

_____!

You can read, write and spell words with these sounds.

_____

Signed **Bet** 😊 _____ and _____ (Class Teacher)

Date _____

Well done

_____!

You can read, write and spell words with these sounds.

_____

Signed **Alf** 😊 _____ and _____ (Class Teacher)

Date _____

Name:_____

oo as in book

oo

oo

How many words can you make?

w
h
l
t
b
c
sh
g

oo

k
l
d

Bet

_____ _____ _____ _____ _____

_____ _____ _____ _____ _____

Now put the words in the gaps.

1. Dad will _____ fish and chips.
2. I read my _____.
3. We _____ the dog for a walk.
4. Little Red Riding _____ met the wolf
5. Use your eyes to _____.
6. The wet dog _____ himself dry.
7. We get _____ from sheep.
8 We burn _____ on the fire.

Look in the book and sort out the OO words

Colour the 'OO' words in Sid Snake

koosh
koor
koco
dogo
dotos
rboko

tofo
oobk
rokoc
hoko
oowd
ohod

dorookoohood
footnstoo
footkefootk
epodeytookrgoodpwooldbookrgoodaytookrnpwooldbookocookokornpwooldbookshooksookoco
trshooks

_____ _____ _____ _____

_____ _____ _____ _____

Name:_____

Read this and underline the oo words.

I looked in a book and saw Little Red Riding Hood. She took cakes she had cooked to her gran. They looked really good. In the Wood stood a wolf, who by hook or by crook wanted Red Riding Hood for his tea.

Write the words you found here.

_____ _____

_____ _____ _____

_____ _____ _____

How many oo words can you find? [ ]

Draw each of these.

 Alf

s	l	g	o	f	o	o	d
b	o	o	k	o	f	n	r
w	o	o	l	o	i	h	o
o	k	d	o	t	s	o	o
t	o	o	k	w	h	o	k
o	n	b	r	o	o	k	a
h	o	o	d	o	o	o	i
s	t	o	o	d	k	o	r

a book	a cook	a wood
a foot	a crook	a hook

Sort out these sentences.

1. my coat. I on have a hood

_____

2. a book. Tom reads in bed

_____

3. put foot. I my on my shoe

_____

4. gold the ring. took The crook

_____

 Bet

Now collect oo words from your reading book

8

Name:_____

How many words can you make?

p   f   b   u   ll   ing   ed

_____   _____   _____   _____

Find the right ending for the sentences.

1. The door said   full of milk.

2. The bull had a   weeds in the garden.

3. The horse was   Pull not Push.

4. The glass was   ring in it's nose.

5. Mum pulled up the   pulling the cart.

Write the sentences here.

1._____

2._____

3._____

4._____

5._____

Sort out these words.

lupl

ulfl

nigpllu

edlpul

lubl

_____ _____

_____ _____ _____

Now draw a field full of flowers and a boy pulling the gate shut.

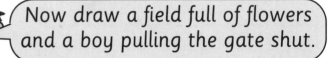

   9

Name:_____

Alf: Read the story carefully. Put a ring around the oo and u words that are spelt wrongly.

Bet: Then write the story out correctly.

I pooled on my coat and hud and tuk

_____

myself to the library to luk for a gud buk.

_____

I found a buk fool of pictures of buls.

_____

I tuk mum a cuk buk. It all luked gud!

_____

Find words that rhyme.

Bet: Colour the 'oo' words and 'u' words in Sid Snake.

book	pull	hood
____	____	____
____	____	____

Alf: Find 'oo' and 'u' words in the grid. How many 'oo' words? [ ]

How many 'u' words? [ ]

o	f	f	s	h	o	o	k
p	p	u	l	l	i	n	g
o	f	l	i	g	d	l	o
b	u	l	l	i	r	o	o
o	l	u	n	w	o	o	d
o	l	o	c	o	o	k	o
k	i	t	o	o	k	u	r
u	p	u	l	l	t	o	o

andapnbpoobgpooghoodpulledneecookahookiupullingowoodofulletookitlookbulloshootahoo

Name:_____

How many words can you make?

c
h   p   d   st
  b   sh f

ar

k   d
  m
    p

_____ _____ _____ _____

_____ _____ _____ _____

Now put the words in the gaps.

1. A _____ shines in the night sky.

2. Pigs and sheep live on a _____.

3. We play on the swings in the _____.

4. The dog _____s loudly.

5. Look at all my birthday _____s.

6. This knife is _____.

7. At night it is _____.

8. The sum was _____ and I could not do it.

Bet

Find the words that rhyme.

mark	arm
art	car
harp	arch

Write the words for the pictures.

Sort out the words in the stars

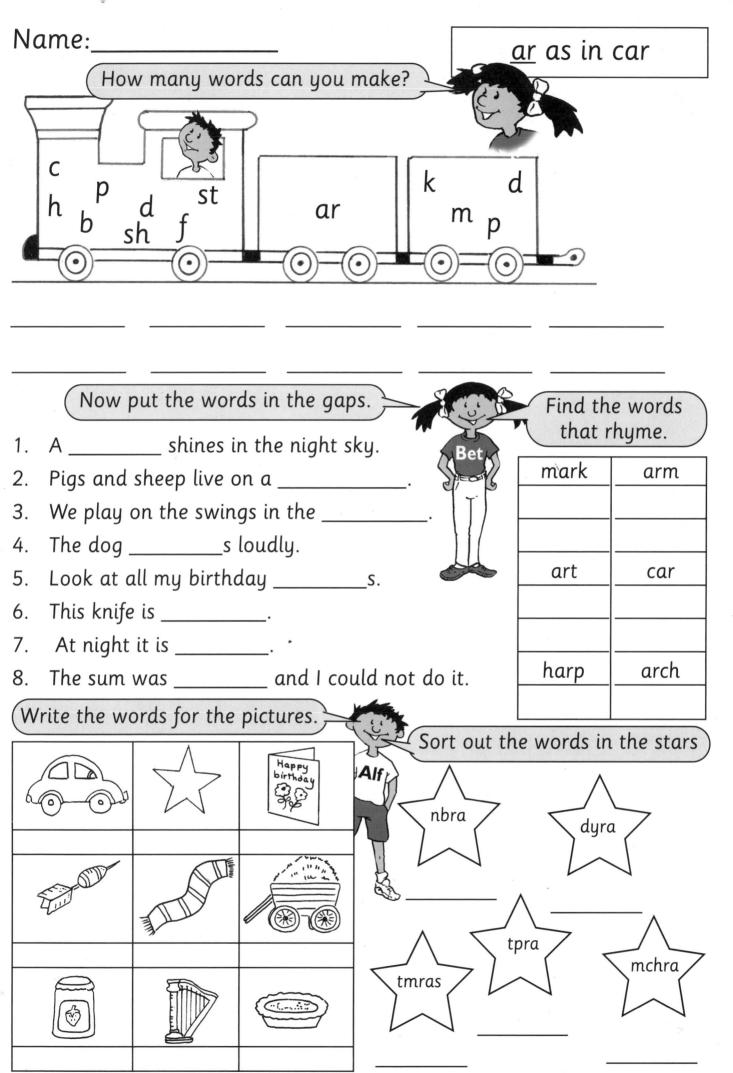

Alf

nbra

dyra

_____

tpra

tmras

mchra

_____

_____

_____

Name:_____

Look at the pictures. Answer in sentences.

1. Where are the cats?
   The cats are on the _____.

2. Where are the flowers?

   _____

3. Where are the sheep?

   _____

4. Where are the darts?

   _____

5. Where are the stars?

   _____

a	s	h	e	h	a	r	m
r	g	a	r	d	e	n	a
p	a	s	b	a	r	n	r
e	r	h	e	r	a	t	k
a	p	a	r	k	r	a	o
y	a	r	d	a	t	r	r
o	r	k	a	t	r	t	p
c	h	a	r	m	r	a	t

Find the 'ar' words

Now put in the missing letters.

g _ _ _ _ _

b _ _ _

p _ _ _

sh _ _ _

d _ _ _

t _ _ _

ch _ _ _

h _ _ _

m _ _ _

Now use your reading book to find 'ar' words. Put them in the shark.

Name:_____

How many words can you make?

b
j
l
c   r
ann   t   enj

oy

al
ing

_____ _____ _____ _____ _____

_____ _____ _____ _____ _____

Put a ring around the 'oy' words.

I know a boy, called Roy, who likes cowboy films. He jumped for joy when his mum bought him a toy horse. He was annoyed when the cowboy film was not on. He is a loyal fan.

Now choose any 5 'oy' words and write them in sentences.

1. _____
2. _____
3. _____
4. _____
5. _____

Sort out the words in the toy cars.

Fill in the missing letters.

oby

_____

nanyo

_____

yalor

_____

yoj

_____

jnoye

_____

ayoll

_____

					b		
					_		_
e	_	_	o	y	_	n	_
				o			n
r	_	y	_	_			_
							y

enjoying
Make words out of this word. How many can you make?

Name:_____

Sort out the sentences.

1. toy. playing The baby with is the

_____

2. films. watching enjoy cowboy I

_____

3. a royal The Queen lady. is

_____

4. is annoyed. When is cross he my teacher

_____

5. loyal Sam a dog. is

_____

Find the 'oy' words in the grid

Now put in the missing letters.

e	n	j	o	y	g	o	e
r	l	o	y	a	l	y	n
b	o	y	t	n	e	o	j
c	y	d	y	n	g	j	o
l	a	o	i	o	t	o	y
a	l	r	o	y	a	l	i
c	o	w	b	o	y	t	n
a	n	n	o	y	i	n	g

a _ _ _ _ _

e _ _ _ _ _ _ _

b _ _

l _ _ _ _

c _ _ _ _ _

r _ _ _ _

j _ _

t _ _

e _ _ _ _

a _ _ _ _ _ _ _ _

Find the 'oy' words
in Sid Snake

aboyaloyalarcowboyocsoiroyalarannoyingotoyojoyr

Name:_____

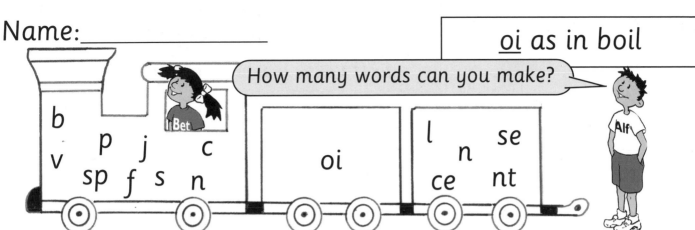

How many words can you make?

b
v
p
j
c
sp f s n

oi

l
n se
ce nt

Find the right ending for the sentences.

1. 100 pennies ------------------------------- a sharp point.
2. The kettle ------------------------ make a pound coin.
3. The dog digs   the cubs tonight.
4. Sam is joining   is boiling.
5. My pencil has   in the soil

Now, write the sentences here.

1. _____

2. _____

3. _____

4. _____

5. _____

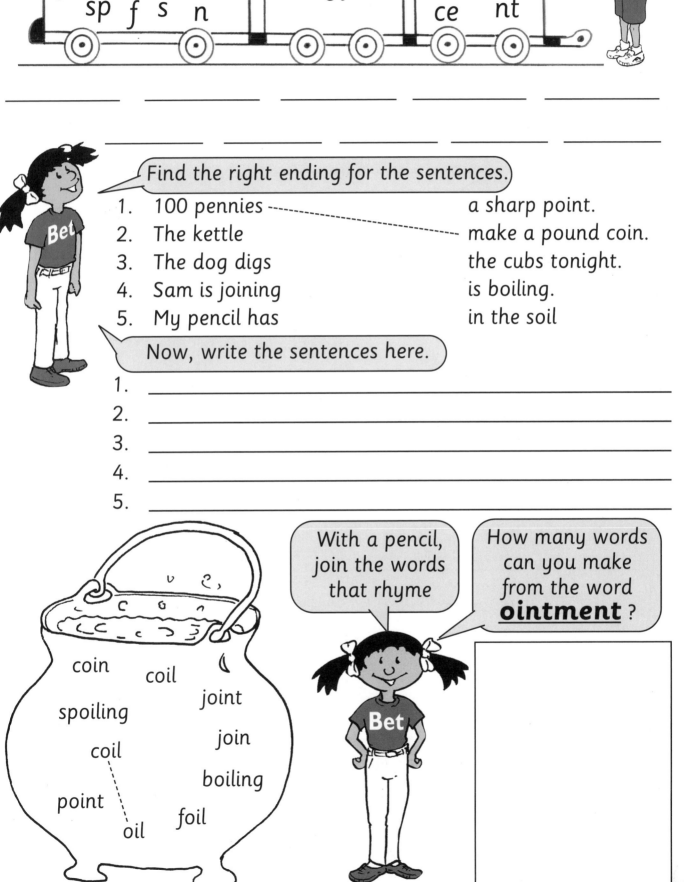

With a pencil, join the words that rhyme

How many words can you make from the word **ointment** ?

coin
coil
joint
spoiling
join
coil
boiling
point
foil
oil

15

Name:_____

Put a ring around the words spelt wrongly, then write each sentence correctly

1. Tom is joyning a swimming club.

_____

2. Do not make a noyse!

_____

3. Ben was spoyling the game.

_____

4. The poynter told us it was one o'clock.

_____

5. The man gave the boy a 50p coyne.

_____

Draw these.

Fill in the missing letters.

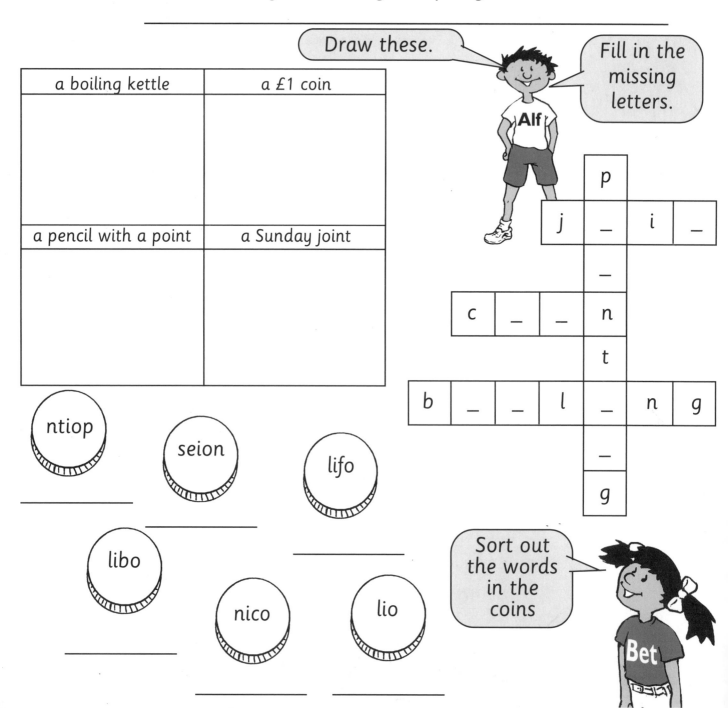

a boiling kettle	a £1 coin
a pencil with a point	a Sunday joint

Sort out the words in the coins

ntiop _____

seion _____

lifo _____

libo

nico _____

lio

© Topical Resources. May be photocopied for classroom use only.

Name:_____

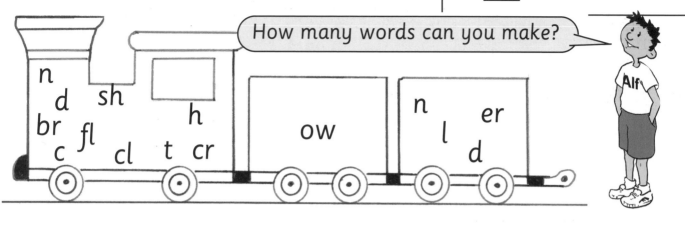

How many words can you make?

n d sh br fl c cl t cr h   ow   n l d er

_____ _____ _____ _____ _____

_____ _____ _____ _____ _____

Put a ring around the 'OW' words.

A clown saw a brown cow in a field of flowers. In a tree, an owl looked down and said, "How do you dooo....?" A shower of rain came down and the clown went back to 'Blackpool Tower' to make the crowd laugh.

Now choose any 5 'OW' words and write them in sentences.

1. _____

2. _____

3. _____

4. _____

5. _____

Find th 'OW' words in the grid.

Find words that rhyme.

t	o	w	n	s	r	o	w
a	n	d	t	h	e	w	c
i	t	f	l	o	w	e	r
o	b	r	o	w	n	c	o
n	h	h	e	e	o	a	w
t	o	w	e	r	n	t	d
a	w	i	c	l	o	w	n
o	l	i	t	r	o	n	e

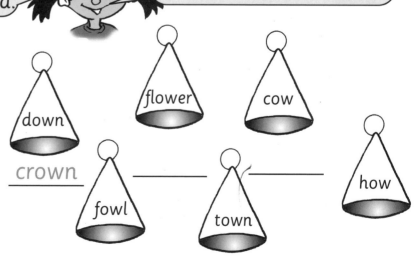

down   flower   cow

crown _____   fowl   town   how

_____ _____ _____

© Topical Resources. May be photocopied for classroom use only.   17

Name:_____

Draw these.

ow as in town

Sort out these '**ow**' words.

a brown cow	a flower	an owl
a clown	a shower	a crowd

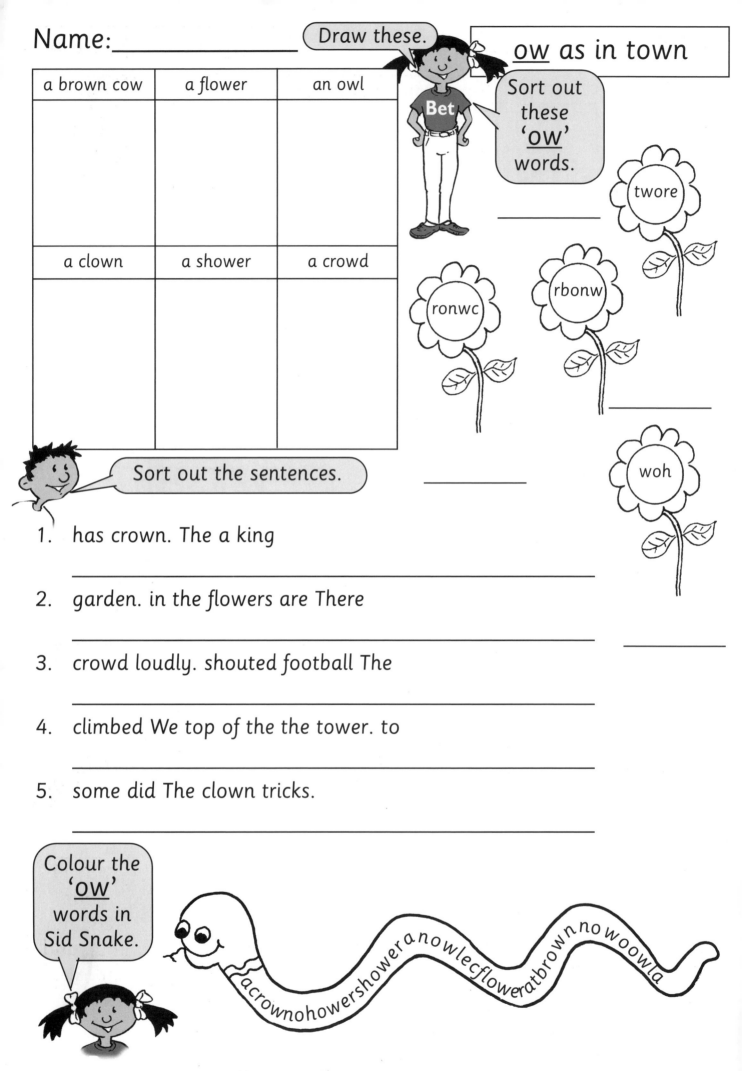

twore

rbonw

ronwc

woh

_____

_____

_____

_____

Sort out the sentences.

1. has crown. The a king

_____

2. garden. in the flowers are There

_____

3. crowd loudly. shouted football The

_____

4. climbed We top of the the tower. to

_____

5. some did The clown tricks.

_____

Colour the '**ow**' words in Sid Snake.

acrownohowershoweranowlecfloweratbrownnowoowla

Name:_____

How many words can you make?

sh
fl gr
  r   m   s
    h   p

ou

r   th
  t
    nd

Bet

_____ _____ _____

_____ _____ _____

Write 5 sentences. Begin each with:-

1. Our house has _____.
2. _____.
3. _____.
4. _____.
5. _____.

Find the pairs of words that rhyme.

out
round   bounce
pounce
our   flour
ground
mouse

house
south
shout
mouth

out		
shout		

Now put in the missing letters.

Alf

Find the 'OU' words.

Bet

s	p	o	u	t	o	l	d
h	c	u	e	r	f	o	o
o	r	t	c	l	o	u	d
u	o	e	o	n	u	d	u
s	u	a	u	s	n	o	n
e	c	r	n	o	d	o	o
n	h	o	t	n	o	u	r
t	r	o	u	s	e	r	s

f _ _ _ _ _
sp _ _ _ _
o _ _
cl _ _ _
tr _ _ _ _ _ _
c _ _ _ _
h _ _ _ _
l _ _ _
o _ _
cr _ _ _ _

Look in your reading book and find 'ou' words.

19

Name:_____

Draw these.

colour the 'OU' words in the scarf.

a mouse	a house	a big mouth
a cloud	trousers	a hound

Alf

outigroundpoundtooba
cloudotloutenbouncescoutoo
trousersonourisoundip

Find the right ending for the sentences.

Bet

1. A circle is a   make an hour.
2. We bounce   a pouch.
3. A tea-pot has   round shape.
4. Sixty minutes   the big red ball.
5. A kangaroo has   a spout.

Now write the sentences here.

1. _____.
2. _____.
3. _____.
4. _____.
5. _____.

Sort out the 'ou' words

ondup

loufr

tou

suome

_____

rou

ntouc

houst

_____

onfud

_____   _____

© Topical Resources. May be photocopied for classroom use only.

Name:_____

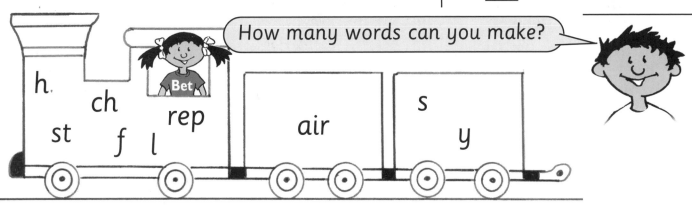

How many words can you make?

h. ch st f l rep air s y

___ ___ ___ ___

___ ___ ___ ___

Now put the words in the gaps.

Colour the 'air' words in Sid Snake.

1. I sit on a _____ .

2. I have a _____ of shoes.

3. We go on rides at the _____.

4. Bet brushed her _____.

5. Mum _____ the broken toy.

6. A fox lives in a _____.

7. The tooth _____ brings money.

8. We go up _____ to bed.

Find the 'air' words.

Now put in the missing letters

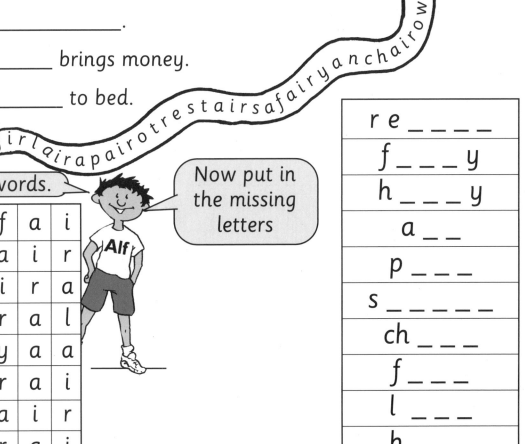

h	a	i	r	o	f	a	i
s	t	i	a	r	a	i	r
t	r	e	p	a	i	r	a
a	r	i	a	p	r	a	l
i	h	a	i	r	y	a	a
r	a	o	r	t	r	a	i
s	w	a	i	f	a	i	r
a	c	h	a	i	r	a	i

r e _ _ _ _
f _ _ _ y
h _ _ _ y
a _ _
p _ _ _
s _ _ _ _ _
ch _ _ _
f _ _ _
l _ _ _
h _ _ _

Name:_____

Put a ring round the 'air' words.

In a fairy story book I have upstairs, there is a picture of a pair of fairies with golden hair. Both are standing on silver chairs, waving their wands in the air. There is also a story about a hairy monster who lives in a secret lair.

Now choose any 5 'air' words and write each in a sentence.

1. _____.
2. _____.
3. _____.
4. _____.
5. _____.

Fill in the missing letters.

Draw these.

	a chair	a hairy monster
c	h	_	_	r
s	_	r		
t	_			

r | _ | p | _ | i | r

Sort out these words

a chair	a hairy monster
a fairy	a girl with brown hair

h | _ | _ | r | _

ria ___

raich ___

riaf ___

aipr ___

riafy ___

Name:_____

How many words can you make?

h
c b
r st f d
sh gl squ Cl

| are | d |

Now, put the words in the gaps.

Colour the 'are' words in Sid Snake.

1. Please _____ the sweets.

2. How much is the bus _____ .

3. A shape with four equal sides is a _____.

4. A girl's name is _____.

5. Take _____ when you cross the road.

6. To _____ to do something is very brave.

7. To look hard is to _____.

8. Something not found often is _____ .

tglareadsquaretshareatcarebatbarearaaredarendfarentstareatclaresat

Find the 'are' words.

Put in the missing letters

s	g	l	a	r	e	b	c
q	u	r	a	s	t	a	l
u	o	e	s	h	a	r	a
a	p	s	t	a	r	e	r
r	a	r	a	r	e	a	e
e	f	a	r	e	n	s	b
d	a	r	e	b	t	e	r
e	r	a	r	c	a	r	e

st _ _ _   r _ _ _

Cl _ _ _   squ _ _ _

sh _ _ _   gl _ _ _

b _ _ _   d _ _ _

c _ _ _   f _ _ _

23

Name:_____

are as in care

Underline the 'are' words.

Clare and I share the same hobby. We both care for animals. One day we saw a hare. We did not dare move as we might scare it. We stared as they are so rare and could not bare it when the hare ran away.

Now choose any 5 'are' words and write them in a sentence.

1. _____.
2. _____.
3. _____.
4. _____.
5. _____.

Sort out the 'are' words in the squares.

trase

read

qsruae

hraes

elarg

rbea

_____

_____

f

—

d

—

b a — —

c —

— h — r —

t —

a —

Put 'are' words in the squares.

Words with 4 letters

—

e

Put in the missing letters.

Words with 5 letters

24

Name:_____

Put in the missing letters.

t _ e _ e   _ h e _ e   t _ _ _ e   _ h _ r _
w _ e _ e   _ h _ r e   w _ _ _ e   _ h e _ _

Farmer Smith's field

tree

bird

butterfly

flower

duck

web

leaves

pond

grass

ladybird

spider

Look at the picture. Answer the questions. Begin each ' There are __'

1. Where are 4 butterflies?   1. There are 4 butterflies on the flowers.
2. Where are 3 ducks?   2. _____
3. Where are 2 spiders?   3. _____
4. Where are 3 ladybirds?   4. _____
5. Where are 5 flowers?   5. _____

Find 'where' and 'there'.
How many? 'where' [ ]
         'there [ ]

Put 'where' or 'there' in the gaps.

e	w	t	h	e	r	e	t
t	h	e	r	e	e	w	h
h	e	h	e	r	w	h	e
e	r	r	t	h	h	e	r
r	e	e	t	h	e	r	e
e	h	t	h	e	r	e	r
w	h	e	r	e	e	h	h
t	h	w	h	e	r	e	t

1. _____ are they going?
2. In our class _____ are 10 boys.
3. _____ is my pencil?.
4. _____ are you going on holiday?
5. We went _____ on our trip.
6. Are _____ any sweets left?
7. They were happy to stay _____.
8. _____ is your book?

25

Name:_____

Put a ring around 'where' or 'there'.

"Oh where, oh where, did I put my reading book?" said Tom. "It's over there." said Mum. "Where?" said Tom again. "Over there on the table where you left it!" "Yes, it's there, but where is my pen?"

Now write 6 sentences, three with 'there' and three with 'where' in them.

1. _____

2. _____

3. _____

4. _____

5. _____

6. _____

Put in the missing letters.

Colour 'where' or 'there'.

Bet

wewhererthrwhetherertherawhtherewerethere w
thereerwhererwerhwherertherehtretherewhere

	true	false
1. There are seven in a week.		
2. Hull is where the Queen lives.		
3. A hive is where you find bees.		
4. There are men on the moon.		
5. There are 100 pennies in a pound. . .		

Answer true or false.

Name:_____

How many words can you make?

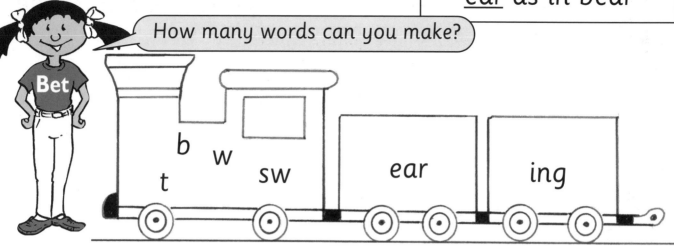

b
t   w   sw   ear   ing

_____   _____   _____

_____

bow   cap   necklace   hat   lead

Look at the pictures. What are they wearing? Answer in sentences.

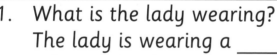

1.   What is the lady wearing?
     The lady is wearing a _____

2.   What is the dog wearing?

_____

3.   What is Bet wearing?

_____

4.   What is the cat wearing?

_____

5.   What is Alf wearing?

_____

rabe   rwae   trae   wsrae   nigraew

_____   _____

Sort out the 'ear' words in the bears.

27

Name:_____

Put the missing letters in the 'ear' words.

b _ _ r   w _ a _   te _ _   s w _ a _

w _ _ r _ n g   t e _ _ i _ g   s w _ _ r _ n _

Find the right endings for the sentences.

1. A bear is a   to swear.
2. We wear shoes   my presents.
3. I tear open   my jeans.
4. It is naughty   large furry animal.
5. I like wearing   on our feet.

Now, write the sentences here.

1. _____
2. _____
3. _____
4. _____
5. _____

Think of 5 things you like wearing.
Begin each sentence with, 'I like wearing ....'

I like wearing my hat.

1. I like wearing _____
2. _____
3. _____
4. _____
5. _____

s	w	a	r	w	e	a	r
w	e	s	a	e	r	w	t
e	a	w	o	a	e	r	o
a	t	e	a	r	i	n	g
r	a	a	t	i	i	o	b
i	i	r	o	n	o	w	e
n	r	o	w	g	e	a	a
g	o	t	o	b	e	a	r

Find the 'ear' words.

Name: _____

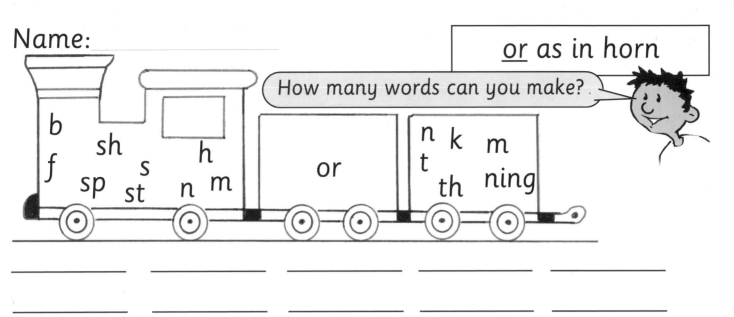

How many words can you make?

b
f
sh
s
sp
st
h
n
m

or

n
t
k
m
th
ning

_____ _____ _____ _____ _____

_____ _____ _____ _____ _____

Find the words that rhyme.

fork
lord
more
sort
cord
horn
born
shore
short
porch
cork
torch

port	pork	corn
___	___	___
___	___	___
sore	sword	scorch
___	___	___
___	___	___

Read this and underline the 'or' words.

This morning it was 'Sports Day'. I put on my shorts and ran until I was worn out. My class score was more than ever before but my legs were sore!. Then a storm came and we ran into the porch before we got wet.

Now choose any 5 'or' words and write them in sentences.

1. _____

2. _____

3. _____

4. _____

5. _____

Colour the 'or' words.

horseaforedshortopcornotcorkoporkitsortom
orningokbornilordofromoresport

29

Name:_____

Put in the missing letters.

Draw these.

a horse	shorts	a sword
a fork	a pork chop	a torch

Crossword letters:
h, o (top)
h — (m o _ e)
r (_ n)
s _ o _ t
e (n)
(i)
b _ _ n
r g

Put a ring around the 'or' words spelt wrongly. Then write each sentence correctly.

1. Tom has towrn his shorts.

_____

2. This moning there was a stawm.

_____

3. In the field of corrn, a mouse was boren.

_____

4. The car beeps it's hawrn.

_____

5. The brave Lorrd has a soword.

_____

Sort out these 'or' words.

sreot

prots

ncro

hrotn

Now look in your reading book and find 'or' words.

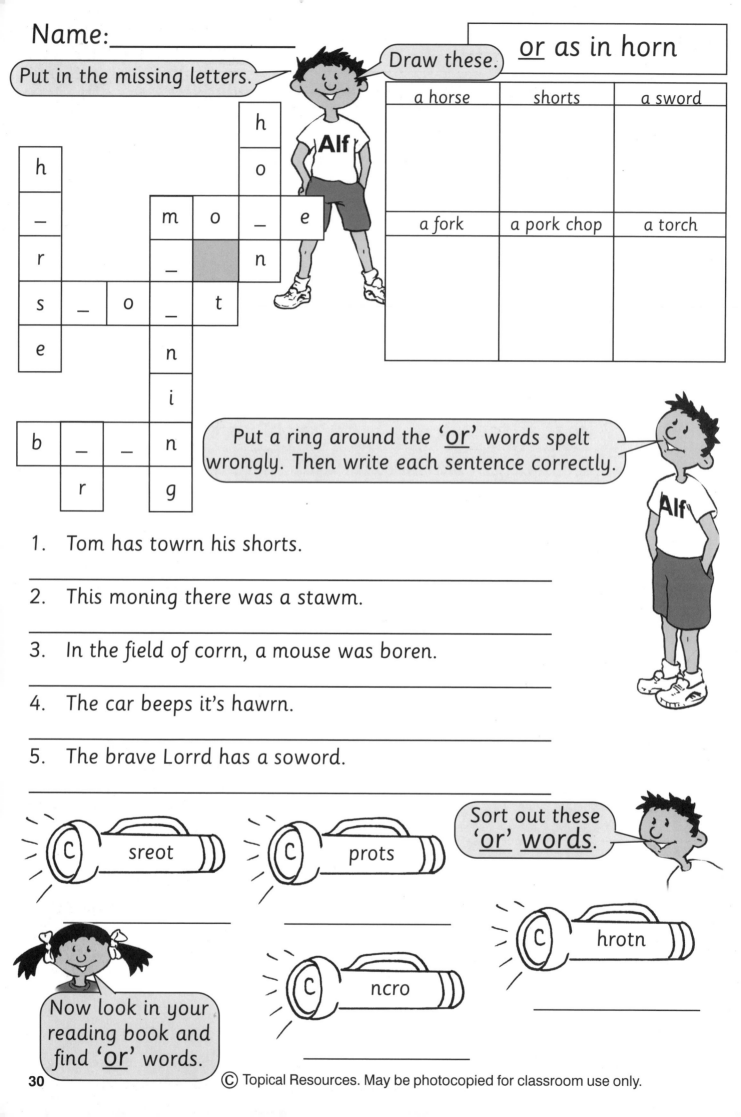

Name:_____

Can you build 4 'oor' words?

d

fl   p

   m

oor

Find the right ending for the sentences.

1. Every room
2. We put carpet
3. To have very little money
4. We find grass and heather

on a moor.
is to be poor.
has a door.
on the floor.

Now write them here.

1. _____
2. _____
3. _____
4. _____

Put in the missing letters.

Colour the 'oor' words.

Sort out the 'oor' words in the doors.

rolof ○

odor ○

oopr ○

romo ○

_____   _____   _____   _____

31

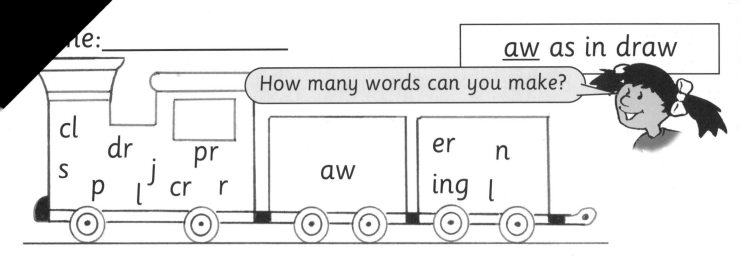

le:_____

How many words can you make?

cl
s
dr
p
j
l
pr
cr
r

aw

er
ing
n
l

Find the words that rhyme.

raw	shawl	dawn
___	___	___
___	___	___
___	pawing	___
___	___	___
___	___	___

jaw
lawn
bawl
pawn
claw
drawing
straw
spawn
paw
yawn
sawing
prawn
crawl
draw

Sort out the sentences.

1. under A prawn the sea. lives

_____

2. pictures. to draw like I

_____

3. brother can baby My crawl.

_____

4. had a dog The sore paw.

_____

5. drink the lemonade We straw. with a

_____

Colour the 'aw' words in the saw.

asawifdrawalawitcrawlalalawnoshawl
ojawaclawonyawnopaworprawnatil

Name:_____

Put a ring around the 'aw' words.

Mr. Law liked to draw eagles with sharp claws, cats sitting in straw licking their paws, frog spawn and prawns. Once, at dawn, he saw a shark with huge jaws. He liked to draw all he saw.

Write the words you found here.

_____ _____ _____

_____ _____ _____

Mr. Law's Farm

field

cow

sheep

Alf

pig

mouse

cat

hen

Write about what Alf saw at the farm.
Begin each sentence with 'Alf saw _____'

Alf saw _____

_____

_____

_____

_____

wrad

lwan

tawrs

_____ _____ _____

Sort out the 'aw' words in Jaws.

rcwal

rpawn

_____ _____

33

Name:_____

au as in caught

How many words can you make?

c d p n t s bec | au Au | ght se ce cer gust | y er

_____ _____ _____ _____

_____ _____ _____ _____

Now put the words in the gaps.

1. I like tomato _____ on my chips.

2. We go on holiday in the month of _____.

3. Put your cup on a _____.

4. Our teacher _____ us to read.

5. We have both a son and a _____.

6. Mum was cross as Alf had been _____.

7. Ann _____ the ball in both hands.

8. "You must go to bed _____ it is late," said Mum..

Colour 'because' in Sid Snake. Look carefully! Is it spelt correctly?

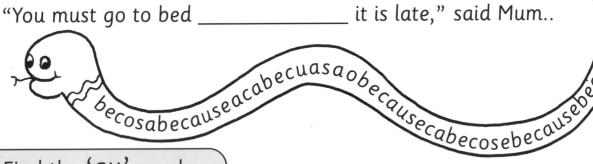

becosabecauseacabecuasaobecausecabecosebecausebecusbecause

Find the 'au' words.

Now put in the missing letters

s	a	u	c	e	r	b	n
p	u	g	a	d	a	e	a
a	g	a	u	a	t	e	u
u	u	t	s	u	a	c	g
s	s	a	e	g	u	a	h
e	t	c	a	u	g	h	t
s	a	u	c	e	h	s	y
d	a	u	g	h	t	e	r

d a _ g _ t _ _
n _ _ g h _ _
c _ _ g h t
t _ _ g h _
s _ _ c _ _
s _ _ c _
A _ g _ s _
p _ _ s _
c _ _ s _

Name:_____

maths
5+3=☐
10-2=☐

music

pets

reading

playing football

art

P. E.

au as in caught

swimming

Bet

Choose 5 things you like doing. Write a sentence beginning, "I like _____ because _____"

1. I like _____

2. _____

3. _____

4. _____

5. _____

Find the right ending for the sentences.

Alf

1. An author ----------------- not to behave.

2. To pause is to ----------- writes books.

3. Cause is to make stop for a short time.

4. To be naughty is a haunted house.

5. The ghost lived in something happen.

Now write them here.

1. _____

2. _____

3. _____

4. _____

5. _____

spaue   cabesue   gthauc   usaec   ttuahg   gAuust

Sort out the 'au' words.

Alf

_____   _____   _____

Name:_____

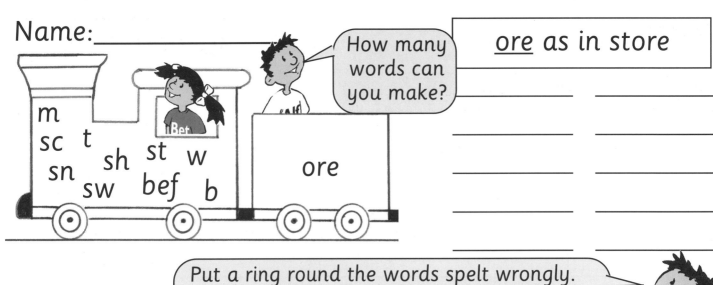

How many words can you make?

ore as in store

m sc t sh st w sn sw bef b

ore

_____ _____

_____ _____

_____ _____

_____ _____

_____ _____

Put a ring round the words spelt wrongly.
Then, write each sentence correctly.

1. Would you like some mor?

_____

2. The dog had a sowr paw.

_____

3. The football scor was a draw.

_____

4. We dig in the sand at the sea shorr.

_____

5. Dad gave a loud snowr in his sleep.

_____

Find the 'ore' words.

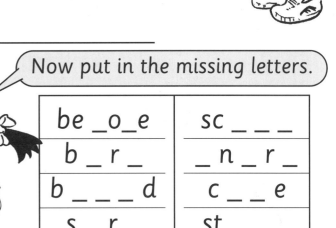

Now put in the missing letters.

b	o	r	e	b	r	o	s
e	e	c	o	r	e	s	b
f	s	c	o	r	e	n	o
o	h	w	o	r	e	o	r
r	o	b	e	s	o	r	e
e	r	t	o	r	e	e	d
b	e	s	t	m	o	r	e
s	c	s	t	o	r	e	d

be _o_e	sc _ _ _
b _ r _	_ n _ r _
b _ _ _ d	c _ _ e
s _ r _	st _ _ _
s h o _ _	m _ _ _
w _ _ _	t _ r _

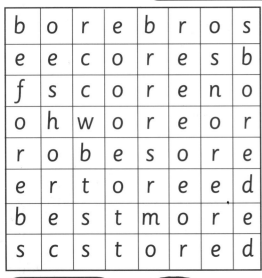

Colour the 'ore' words in Sid

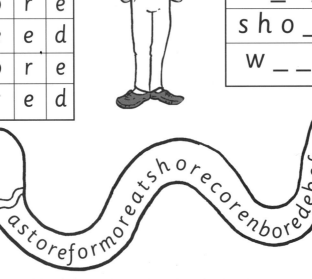

astoreformoreatshorecorenboredebeforescoreelsnorenoter

Name:_____

Put a ring round the 'ore' words.

Mrs. Core said, "I have a treat in store! Mr. Core, don't sit there and snore you awful old bore! Let's go to the sea-shore!" She wore a new hat and without a word more she tore out of the door!

Now choose any 5 'ore' words and write them in sentences.

1. _____

2. _____

3. _____

4. _____

5. _____

How many words can you make?

Fill in the missing words

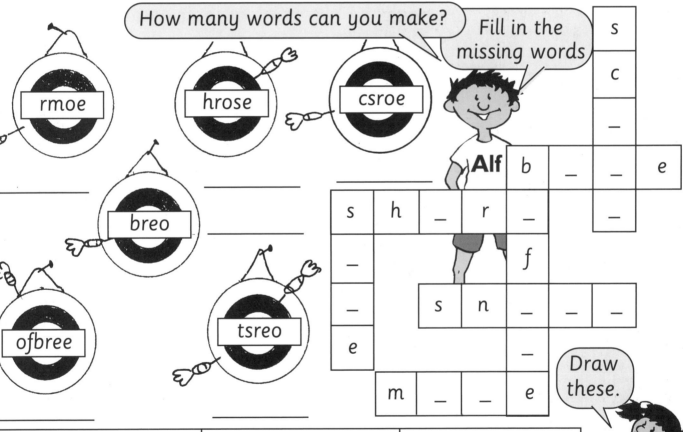

rmoe _____

hrose _____

csroe _____

breo _____

ofbree _____

tsreo _____

Crossword letters:
s
c
—
b _ _ e
—
s h _ r _
— f
— s n _ _ _
— —
e —
m _ _ e

Draw these.

a football score	a sea-shore	a toy store

Name: _____

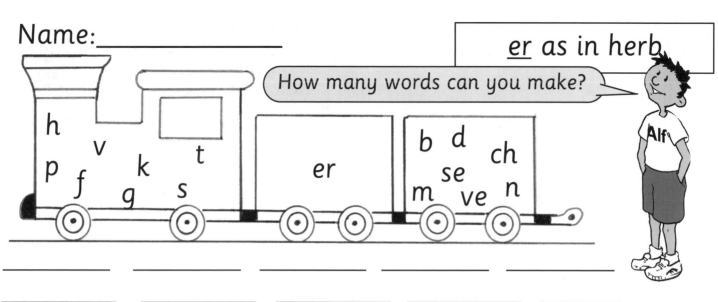

How many words can you make?

h
p
v
f
k
g
t
s

er

b d
ch
se
m ve n

Alf

Find the right ending for the sentences.

Bet

1. A herb grows   on a perch.
2. We saw a herd   you will get germs.
3. My mum had her   in the garden.
4. Wash you hands or   hair permed.
5. The bird sat   of cows.

Now write the sentences in here.

1. _____
2. _____
3. _____
4. _____
5. _____

p	e	r	m	h	e	r	b
e	g	e	r	m	v	e	m
r	r	e	s	t	e	r	m
c	t	m	o	r	r	o	r
h	r	k	e	s	b	m	f
e	e	e	r	r	e	e	e
v	e	r	s	e	r	r	r
r	e	b	e	h	e	r	n

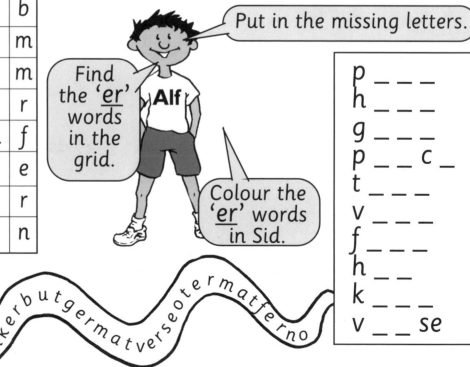

Put in the missing letters.

Find the 'er' words in the grid.

Alf

Colour the 'er' words in Sid.

p _ _ _
h _ _ _
g _ _ _
p _ _ c _
t _ _ _
v _ _ _
f _ _ _
h _ _ _
k _ _ _
v _ _ se

aherdbpermumkerbutgermatverseotermatferno

Name:_____

Practise writing these words.

mother   father   water   after   November
_____   _____   _____   _____   _____

Summer   December   Letter   Under   September
_____   _____ _____   _____   _____

Draw these

a flower	a letter	a monster
butter	the teacher	a pair of trainers

Find a word that rhymes in the flower.

power	letter	kipper
_____	_____	_____
speaker	stronger	mutter
_____	_____	_____
lighter	rather	drummer
_____	_____	_____

Flower petals: better, beaker, longer, butter, flower, father, tighter, flipper, summer

Now, using your reading book, collect words that end in 'er'.

Sort out these months.

eptSmebre	tcObroe
_____	_____
vebNomer	cDeebmer
_____	_____

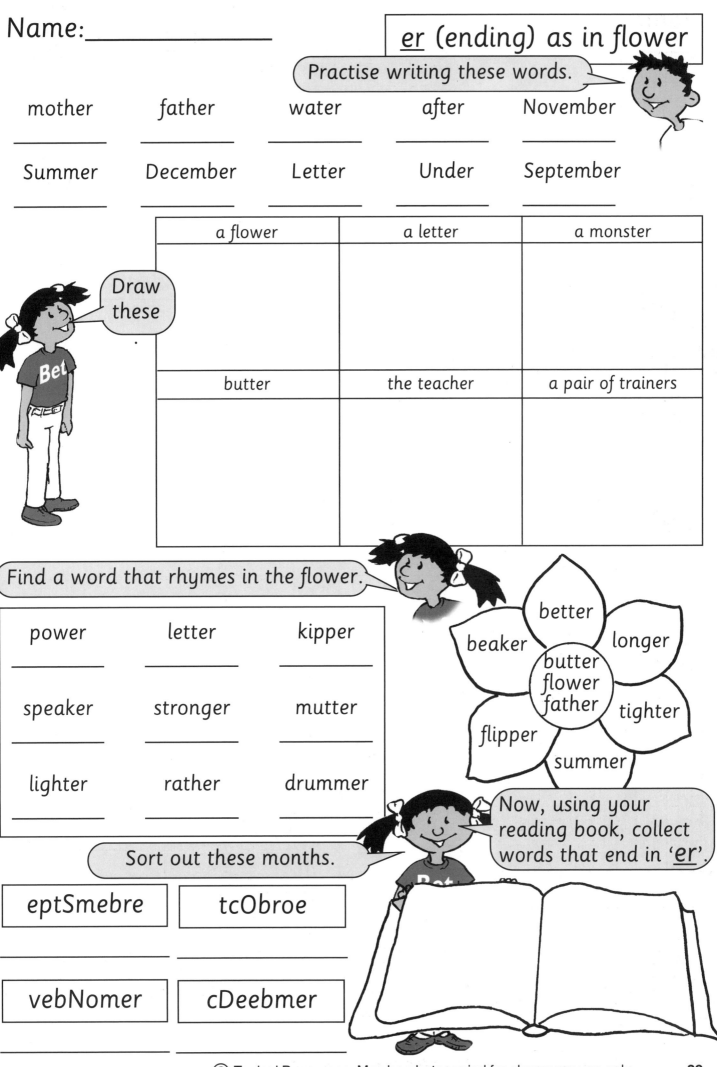

39

Name:_____

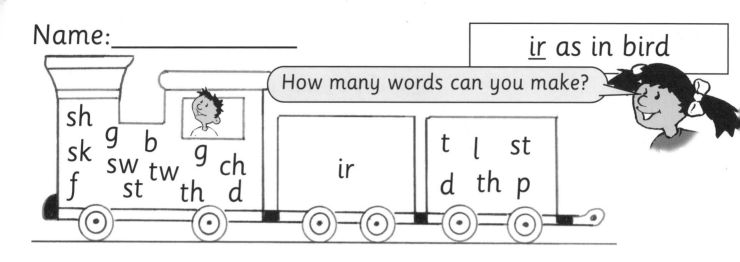

How many words can you make?

sh sk f g sw st b tw g ch th d

ir

t l st d th p

_____ _____ _____ _____ _____

_____ _____ _____ _____

Put the words in the gaps.

1. There is a _____ up in the tree.

2. He was _____ in the race.

3. Dad gave Alf a new _____ to wear.

4. Today is my _____ day.

5. A Christmas tree is a _____ tree.

6. " _____ the soup," said Dad.

7. Mum went to town to buy a new _____.

8. The _____ is called Emma.

b	s	i	t	o	s	r	a
i	r	o	r	s	k	i	r
r	i	l	s	w	i	r	l
d	r	t	h	i	r	d	f
g	i	r	i	r	t	i	i
i	r	r	r	l	i	r	r
r	i	s	t	i	r	t	s
l	b	i	r	t	h	i	t

Find the 'ir' words

Fill in the missing letters.

th _ _ d   b _ _ t h
sk _ _ _   f _ _ _ t
st _ _   d _ _ _
g _ _ _   sw _ _ l
sh _ _ _   b _ _ _

Colour the 'ir' words in Sid

asirifireshoreoshirtobebirdothirstopskirtenfirstiptwirleto

Name:_____

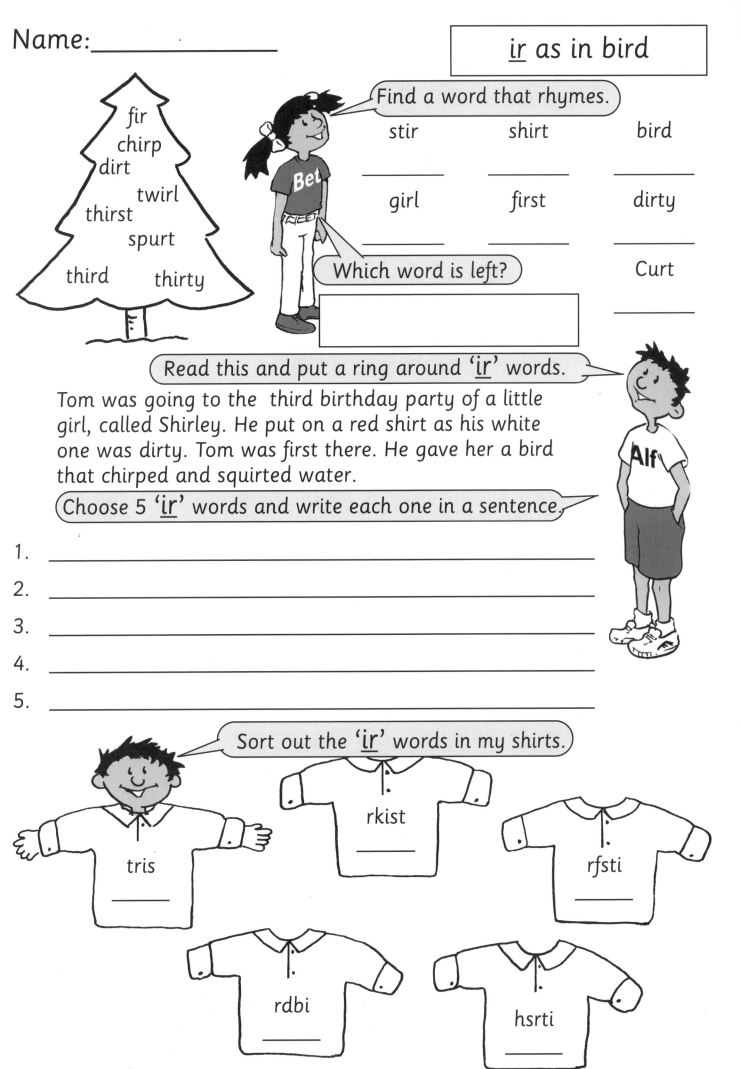

fir
chirp
dirt
twirl
thirst
spurt
third   thirty

Find a word that rhymes.

stir	shirt	bird
____	____	____
girl	first	dirty
____	____	____
		Curt
		____

Which word is left?

Read this and put a ring around 'ir' words.

Tom was going to the third birthday party of a little girl, called Shirley. He put on a red shirt as his white one was dirty. Tom was first there. He gave her a bird that chirped and squirted water.

Choose 5 'ir' words and write each one in a sentence.

1. _____
2. _____
3. _____
4. _____
5. _____

Sort out the 'ir' words in my shirts.

tris
____

rkist
____

rfsti
____

rdbi
____

hsrti
____

41

Name:_____

How many words can you make?

ch
c b n
h f sp t p   ur   n f ly
                  ch se t
                  ve st

Bet

_____ _____ _____ _____ _____ _____

_____ _____ _____ _____ _____

Put the words in the gaps.

Alf

1. We go to _____ on Sunday.
2. The lady wore a coat made of _____ .
3. I _____ my leg when I fell.
4. A _____ works in a hospital.
5. Put your money in your _____.
6. Be careful you do not _____ in the sun.
7. Susan has lovely _____y hair.
8. Suddenly, the balloon _____.

Find a words that rhyme.

turn

hurl

turning

purse

spurt

fur

burn   curl   spur

_____   _____   _____

nurse   burning   hurt

_____   _____   _____

Draw these.

a church	a fur coat	a turkey	a curly haired boy

Name:_____

Draw these.

a nurse	a bonfire burning	a purse	a purring cat

Find the right ending for the sentences.

1. We put curtains ----- for Christmas dinner.
2. I go to school   the weekend.
3. To return is   on the windows.
4. Saturday is at   on Thursday.
5. We have turkey   to come back.

Write the sentences here.

1. _____
2. _____
3. _____
4. _____
5. _____

Put in the missing letters.

t		
_		b
p	_	r	r	u
		f	_	_
				_
c	_	_	l	i
h				_
t	u	_	_	_	n	g
_		
c		
_	_	r	t

Colour the 'ur' words in Sid

Name:_____

How many words can you make?

f
y d h
sh t sp g r
n cl

ear   ing

_____ _____ _____

_____ _____ _____

Now, put the words in the gaps.

1. I _____ with my ear.

2. There are twelve months in a _____.

3. We begin writing a letter with the word _____.

4. Susan cried and the _____ rolled down her cheeks.

5. You can see through glass as it is _____.

6. _____ means at the back.

7. A car has a _____ stick.

8. To be afraid is to be filled with _____.

Colour the 'ear' words in Sid.

ashearodearateariprearofearayearugearticlearuspearoear

Sort out the 'ear' words.

rahe

fare

Bet

rrae

rade

_____

arte

larec

raey

parse

grea

_____ _____ _____ _____

44 © Topical Resources. May be photocopied for classroom use only.

Name:_____

Put a ring round the 'ear' words spelt wrongly in my letter.

Write the letter correctly here.

Dear Tom

It is neerly a yeer since I wrote to you! I heer you have got over your feer of spiders! Dad has put a new geer box in our car. At school we made a Viking speer. Grandma has a new heering aid in her eer.

Look forward to heering from you.

Love
Alf.

Find the 'ear' words in the grid and put in the missing letters.

c	h	e	a	r	i	n	g
l	a	r	y	e	a	r	e
e	e	f	e	a	r	a	a
a	t	e	a	r	e	e	r
r	a	s	p	e	a	r	e

Put in the missing letters.

h _ _ _ _ _ _   r _ _ _
cl _ _ _ _   g _ _ _
t _ _ _   y _ _ _
sp _ _ _   f _ _ _

Name:_____

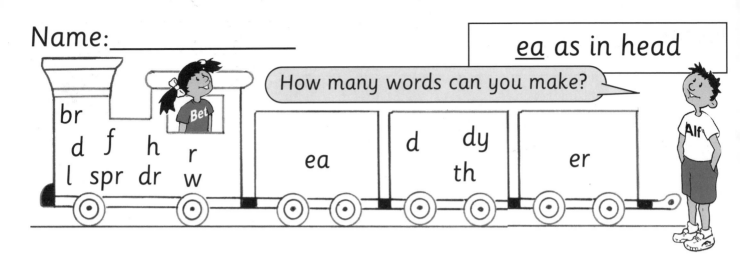

ea as in head

How many words can you make?

br
d f h r
l spr dr w

ea

d dy
th

er

_____ _____ _____ _____ _____

_____ _____ _____ _____

Find the correct ending for the sentences.

1. The weather ---------------------- on my bread.
2. I read   head were blue.
3. I spread butter --------------- was rainy.
4. Alf wore his   a book.
5. The feathers on the bird's   leather jacket

Now write the sentences here.

1. _____
2. _____
3. _____
4. _____
5. _____

Draw these.

a feather	a leather coat
a girl's head	a loaf of bread

Name:_____

Find the words that rhyme.

head   weather

_____   _____

_____   _____

_____   _____

ready   treasure

_____   _____

steady   Heather   read   measure   feather   spread   leather   dead

Sort out the sentences.

1. hot. Today weather is the

_____

2. a box of We found treasure.

_____

3. Mr Fox. Fantastic favourite My book is

_____

4. cut I a bread. slice of

_____

5. were the in meadow. The cows

_____

Find the 'ea' words in the grid.

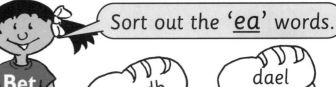

Sort out the 'ea' words.

w	a	h	e	a	v	y	t
e	e	d	e	a	f	d	r
a	b	r	o	n	s	e	e
t	r	e	a	d	a	a	a
h	e	a	d	a	r	t	s
e	a	n	o	e	e	h	u
r	d	e	l	e	a	d	r
p	l	e	a	s	u	r	e

raedb

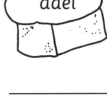
dael

_____

wdoaem

_____

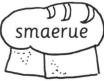
smaerue

_____

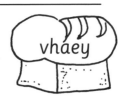
vhaey

_____

fereaht

_____

Revision of long vowel work from Y1 Term 3

Name:_____

Find words that rhyme.

peel tree
deep
keen bee
feet
keep been
feed
seed heel
sheet

feel   seen   sweet

_____   _____   _____

_____   _____   _____

weed   see   sheep

_____   _____   _____

_____   _____   _____

Alf

Now put the words in the gaps.

Bet

1. A _____ stung my arm.
2. I have two _____ .
3. The field was full of _____ .
4. The water is very _____ .
5. The bird is the _____ .
6. I have a white _____ on my bed.
7. We plant _____ in the garden..
8. _____ the potatoes, please.

Sort out the words in the bees

tmee

hcseee

dpsee   _____

Put in the missing letters.

lefe

_____

_____

Find the 'ee' words.

a	f	e	n	r	w	b	n
g	r	e	e	n	e	l	q
o	e	p	e	s	e	e	u
r	e	n	d	t	p	e	e
s	p	e	e	c	h	d	e
c	h	e	e	s	e	o	n
i	n	f	r	e	e	z	e
t	h	r	e	e	a	r	f

Alf

w _ _ p
f r _ _
g r _ _ _
q _ _ _ _
t h _ _ _
b l _ _ d
f r _ _ z _
s p _ _ c h
c h _ _ s _
n _ _ d

ekche

_____

Name:_____ | Revision sheet | ea as in sea

Read the sentences. Put a ring around the 'ea' words that are spelt wrongly. Write them correctly.

1. Today, for a treet, we are going out to tee.

_____

2. We went to the beech and swam in the see.

_____

3. "Your jeens are cleen", said Mum.

_____

4. We had peeches and creem for sweet.

_____

5. "Pleese keep cleen!" said Dad.

_____

6. There are three on eech teem.

_____

Put in the missing letters.   Sort out the 'ea' words.

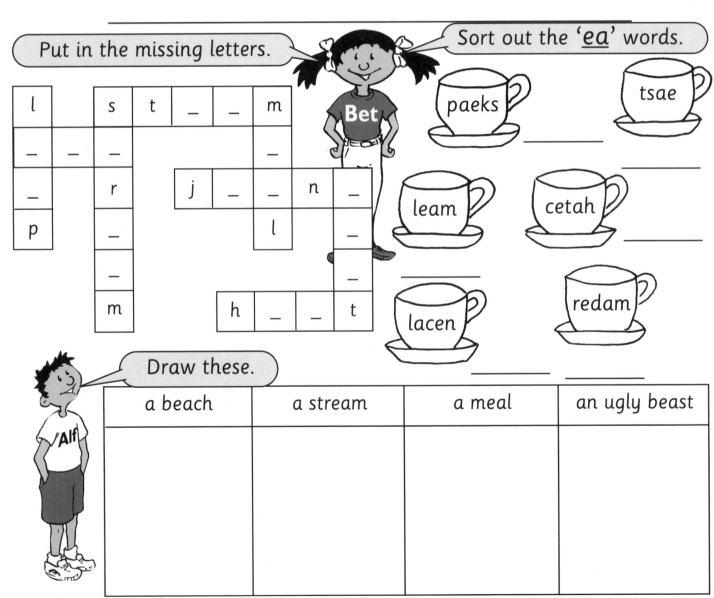

Draw these.

a beach	a stream	a meal	an ugly beast

Name:_____

a	p	a	i	p	i	t	a
r	a	i	l	a	t	a	i
a	i	s	a	i	l	i	s
i	n	a	i	n	i	l	t
n	a	i	l	t	a	i	a
a	i	m	w	a	i	t	i
a	t	r	t	r	a	i	n
m	a	i	d	m	a	i	n

Find the 'ai' words in the grid. Write them here.

Bet

____ ____ ____

____ ____ ____

____ ____ ____

____ ____ ____

Alf

Sort out the muddled sentences.

1. went by We to Spain. train

_____

2. to go sailing boat. on the We paid

_____

3. a trail. made snail The

_____

4. wore a The lady chain. gold

_____

5. goes down The water the drain

_____

6. paid was The maid pounds. twenty

_____

Find the words that rhyme.

train	fail	raise	sailing
____	____	____	____
____	____		
____	____		
____	____		

Bet

paint	maid
____	____
____	____

grain jail pain saint trailing drain snail laid tail paid praise faint wail chain

Name:_____

Put in the missing letters.

```
g _ m _
_     _
  t   k
b     _
t _ k _
h   k
c _ m _
t
_
```

Put the words in the gaps.

1. Lets have a _____ of football.
2. Please shut the _____.
3. I _____ sprouts.
4. I can _____ a cake.
5. Please do not _____ a mess.
6. Tom _____ to my party.
7. The word _____ rhymes with bake.

Draw these.

a whale	a gate	a birthday cake
a snake	a flame	a plate of food

Sort out the 'a - e' words.

msae   klae   pgrae   leapt   tead   mtae

____ ____ ____ ____ ____

Colour the 'a - e' words in Sid Snake.

anameatpalesaleatacameorblamerflakenbrakestapeahatesoplatemnskateashaker

Name:_____ | **Revision sheet** | <u>ay</u> as in day

a	p	a	y	s	a	y	t
s	o	r	p	a	s	o	r
w	s	w	l	r	t	r	a
a	p	a	a	p	r	a	y
y	r	y	y	e	a	r	o
e	a	w	a	y	y	a	b
a	y	r	d	a	y	y	a
m	a	y	e	a	h	a	y

Find the '<u>ay</u>' words.
Write them here.

_____ _____ _____

_____ _____ _____

_____ _____ _____

_____ _____ _____

_____ _____ _____

Find the right ending for the sentences.

1. There are seven days   dog a home.
2. We go to church   hay to eat.
3. Mr Smith gave the stray   in a week.
4. Put the cups on   to pray.
5. Sam gave the horse   the tray.

Now write the sentences here.

1. _____
2. _____
3. _____
4. _____
5. _____

Fill in the missing letters of the days of the week.

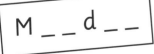 M _ _ d _ _

Tue _ _ a _

W _ dn _ _ d _ _

 Tu _ s _ _ _

F _ _ d _ _

S _ _ u _ d _ _

S _ _ d _ _

53

Name:_____

Put in the missing letters.

```
        l
    t _ _ d
        _
  d _ _ d
      _
p _ _
```

Put the words in the gaps.

1. The boy's rabbit _____.

2. Dad loves to eat pork _____.

3. Emma _____ her shoe laces.

4. Sam tells _____. He does not tell the truth.

Sort out the 'ie' words in the pies.

iep _____

ddei _____

dlie _____

eil _____

tdei _____

ite _____

Bet

Read the sentences. Put a ring round the 'ie' words that are spelt wrongly. Write the sentences correctly.

Alf

1. We had piy and beans for tea.

_____

2. Emma tiyed a ribbon in her hair.

_____

3. "I have no sweets," liyed Tom.

_____

4. Sam cried when his hamster diyed.

_____

Colour the 'ie' words in Sid.

piepipdadiesiytiediliedolievencriedotietidespiedotiedied

Name:_____

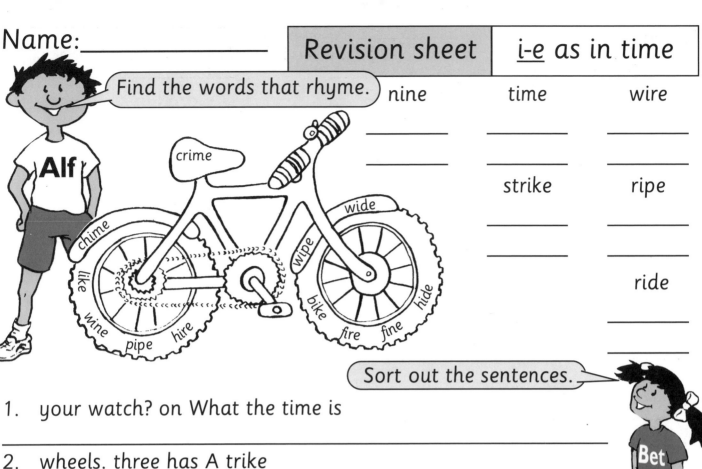

Find the words that rhyme.

nine	time	wire
____	____	____
____	strike	ripe
____	____	____
		ride
		____
		____

Sort out the sentences.

1. your watch? on What the time is

_____

2. wheels. three has A trike

_____

3. wedding. at the The bride beautiful looked

_____

4. chimed clock old The o'clock. three

_____

5. ride. The little donkey had boy a on the

_____

6. had a new Alf bike birthday. for his

_____

Draw these.

a bike	a fire	a pipe
a trike	a slide	a bride

55

Name:_____ | Revision sheet | igh as in night

Put a ring round the 'igh' words.

One night, the moon was shining brightly. I saw a light high up in the sky. "It might be a space-ship on a flight to earth." I said with fright. I wasn't right. "It's a plane!" I said with a slight sigh.

Now choose any 5 'igh' words and write each in a sentence.

1. _____
2. _____
3. _____
4. _____
5. _____

Put in the missing letters.

n
_

s	g
_	_

| _ | l | i | _ | _ | _ |

| i | h |

| h | _ | _ | h |

| h |

| r | _ | g | _ | _ |

e	n	t	i	g	h	t	f
r	i	g	h	t	i	t	r
f	g	l	i	g	h	h	i
l	h	r	i	g	l	i	g
i	t	h	t	h	i	g	h
g	i	g	s	i	g	h	t
h	i	s	i	g	h	e	r
t	m	i	g	h	t	i	h

Find the 'igh' words in the grid.

Sort out the 'igh' words in the 'frightening' ghosts.

fihglt _____

rbghit _____

fgtih _____

ghirt _____

ghsti _____

gmhit _____

Name:_____

Find the words ending in 'y'.

a	f	r	o	p	s	t
n	l	e	s	l	y	f
r	y	s	o	a	b	t
r	s	t	y	t	c	r
s	e	f	n	d	r	y
p	y	f	o	p	y	s
y	t	r	e	m	n	s
s	h	y	e	y	b	y

Alf

Write them here.

_____   _____   _____

_____   _____   _____

_____   _____

_____   _____

Put the words in the gaps.

1. A pig lives in a _____.

2. The baby began to _____.

3. Dad will _____ some bacon.

4. I must _____ hard to learn _____ spellings.

5. _____ means next to.

6. The little boy would not speak as he was very _____.

Sort out the words in the frying pans.

hys _____

psy _____

rfy _____

rty _____

ycr _____

rdy _____

Bet

Colour the words ending in 'y' in Sid.

Draw these.

a sly fox	a frying pan	a pig in a sty	a flying bird

57

Name:_____

Find the words that rhyme.

oat   toast   moan

_____   _____   _____

_____   _____   coach

_____   _____   _____

oak   road   _____

_____   _____   _____

_____   _____

boast
load
toad
float
boat
soak
cloak
roast
coat
coast
groan
poach

Put a ring around the 'oa' words

One day, dad was moaning and groaning with a sore throat, and he could not eat his toast. He put on his coat. "Let's go to the coast," he croaked like a toad. "We could go on a boat!" "Try not to get soaked!" said mum.

Now choose any 5 'oa' words and write each one in a sentence.

1. _____

2. _____

3. _____

4. _____

5. _____

Put in the missing letters.

Draw these.

a croaking toad	a goat
a coach	a boat

© Topical Resources. May be photocopied for classroom use only.

Name:_____

Find the words that rhyme.

cone   rope   hole
lone   cope   throne
stole   pole   home
slope

bone   hope   mole

____   ____   ____

____   ____   ____

____   ____   ____

Which word does not rhyme.

Find the correct ending for each sentence.

1. A king chair
2. A mole digs
3. Another name for a house
4. A long stick is
5. To be by yourself

is a home.
is called a throne.
is to be alone.
holes in the ground.
called a pole.

Now write the sentences here.

1. _____

2. _____

3. _____

4. _____

5. _____

Sort out the 'o-e' words.

phoe

tosne

bnoe

____

nceo

lhoe

____

tsloe

____

____

____

a	l	o	n	e	m	s	n
n	o	t	h	r	o	n	e
r	p	o	l	e	l	o	h
o	s	t	o	n	e	r	o
p	e	s	c	o	p	e	l
e	t	o	s	l	o	p	e

Find the 'o-e' words. Write them here.

____   ____   ____

____   ____   ____

____

59

Name:_____

Find the words that rhyme.

show   flown   flowing

_____   _____   _____

_____   _____   _____

_____   _____   _____

_____   _____

(Snowman words: showing, thrown, row, know, mow, blowing, crow, towing, sown, glowing, known)

Put the words in the gaps.

1. I _____ my 5 x table.
2. The car was _____ a caravan.
3. We have _____ the seeds in the garden.
4. Mum will _____ the lawn.
5. There is a _____'s nest up in the tree.
6. Alf is _____ bubbles.
7. "And pretty maids all in a _____".
8. A light was _____ in the dark.

Sort out the 'ow' words in the bowls.

nwok   _____

rowc   _____

lwos   _____

hsow   _____

lbow   _____

rmwoe   _____

Fill in the missing letters.

m _ w _ r
g
_
b _ _ l
_
k _
n n
s _ _ w i _ g
l _
t _ r _ _ n
_

Draw these.

a snowman	a bowl of fruit	a car towing a caravan	a glowing lamp

Revision sheet | <u>oo</u> as in pool

o	o	o	l	o	r	s	z
o	s	t	o	o	l	o	o
g	p	r	s	o	o	n	o
o	o	o	c	n	m	o	s
o	o	o	h	o	o	p	r
s	n	p	o	n	o	r	o
e	r	o	o	t	n	s	o
t	o	o	l	t	o	k	f

Find the '<u>oo</u>' words.

Write them here.

Bet

_____ _____ _____

_____ _____ _____

_____ _____ _____

_____ _____ _____

Put a ring around the '<u>oo</u>' words.

Alf

One day, we went with school, to visit the zoo. It was too hot! The animals were snoozing and the flowers drooping. To stay cool, a coot swooped into a pool and was chased by a goose. We hooted as he flew back to the roof.

Now choose any 5 '<u>oo</u>' words and write each one in a sentence.

1. _____

2. _____

3. _____

4. _____

5. _____

hoof | moo | school
hoop | spoon
boot | soon
fool | loop | too

Find the words that rhyme.

Alf

snoop	moon
____	____
____	____
zoo	pool
____	____
____	____
root	roof
____	____

Find the words that rhyme.

June   cute

_____   _____

_____   _____

use   _____

_____   rule

cube   _____

_____   cure

_____

chute   mule

tune   brute   flute

tube   fuse

sure   prune

Find the right ending for each sentence.

1. A cube has ----------   a kind of horse.
2. A prune is   six faces.
3. Alf plays a tune   of toothpaste.
4. A mule is   a dried plum.
5. We have a tube   on his flute.

Now, copy them here.

1. _____
2. _____
3. _____
4. _____
5. _____

Put in the missing letters.

		s	
t	_	n	_

| b |
| _ |

| p | _ | _ | n | e |

c		
_		_
r		t
_	l	_
_

rsue   netu

_____   _____

bteu   nJue

_____   _____

              esu

              _____

Sort out the '<u>u - e</u>' words in the tubes.

lmue

_____

Name:_____

Revision sheet

ue as in blue

l	b	l	u	e	r	o	g
a	o	t	d	g	n	e	l
r	n	e	c	l	u	e	u
d	o	r	o	u	t	o	i
u	t	r	u	e	r	e	n
e	o	g	l	u	e	d	g

Bet

Write them here.

_ l _ _   g _ _ _

c _ _ _   g _ _ i n _

t _ _ _   g _ u _ d

d _ _

Put the words in the gaps.

1. The sky is _____ .

2. We stick paper with _____ .

3. We had to answer _____ or false.

4. The bus is _____ to come in a minute.

5. Tom _____ his finger to the card.

Answer true or false.

Alf

	true	false
1. Yellow and black make blue.		
2. We use glue to stick things.		
3. A fact is true.		
4. My front door is blue.		
5. Due is a word with three letters. .		

abluendgelueatrueeredueveclueggluingnorgluedetrruest

Draw a picture with 4 blue things in it.

Alf

Colour blue all the 'ue' words in Sid Snake.

Name:_____

Find the 'ew' words.

a	t	e	n	o	r	s	f
a	h	l	e	n	e	d	l
g	r	e	w	o	s	r	e
t	e	a	r	s	t	e	w
a	w	e	c	h	e	w	e
n	o	w	e	t	w	e	n
b	r	e	w	a	f	e	w
e	o	f	b	l	e	w	e

Write them here.

_____ _____ _____

_____ _____ _____

_____ _____ _____

_____

Sort out the sentences.

1.   blew The wind hat off. the man's

_____

2.   to chew likes a bone. The dog

_____

3.   grew very The sunflower tall.

_____

4.   in the air. the ball up Sam threw

_____

5.   sweets. few a have We

_____

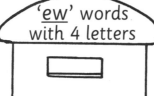

Sort out the 'ew' words on this page.

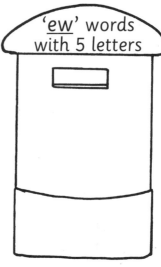

'ew' words
with 3 letters

'ew' words
with 4 letters

'ew' words
with 5 letters